CHIPS

by

SILAS K. HOCKING

AUTHOR OF 'HER BENNY' AND 'CRICKET'

'Memories'

CHIPS was first published in 1894

Illustrated Edition 1895

ISBN 1 899181 04 8

Reprint organised by:

This edition published by:
'Memories'
Dawson Street, Manchester M3 4JZ
Tel: 0161 832 3917

Prepared by:
Northern Publishing Services
28 Bedford Road
Firswood M16 0JA
Tel: 0161 862 9399

Printed & bound by:
Manchester Free Press
Tel: 0161 864 4540

DEDICATION

*Dedicated to the Manchester City Mission of
old and those past miracle workers of the
streets of Salford and Manchester, and to the workers
of Wood Street Mission and the Night Shelters who
carry on the brave and needed work today.*

Silas Kitto Hocking was born on the 24th March 1850 in the village of St. Stephens, Cornwall. The son of a Cornish mine owner he had a protected, middle class, Christian upbringing. Early in life he decided that he was interested in The Church and at the age of 17 was invited to address his local Non-Conformist Chapel.

After two small preaching posts around the country he was over-awed when offered a chance to join the prestigious circuit in Liverpool. Being a stranger to the city he was offered accommodation by the circuit steward Mr Richard Lloyd which he accepted, little knowing that three years later he would marry the daughter. As the youngest preacher he was given the poorest area, the down-town church and two small ones across the water at Birkenhead and Seacombe to look after. It was this post which led him to meeting the waifs and strays of Liverpool's streets that form so much of this book, and his travelling across on the Ferry became part of the story line. He spent three years in Liverpool and wrote about the joy he got from helping the down and out and the relaxation and pleasure of attending the organ recitals in St. George's Hall on his days off. He moved to the circuit in Manchester and spent two years there.

Circuit work was not entirely to his liking, and when he was offered his own church in Burnley he took up the offer. It was there he took up writing as a relaxation. The manuscript was called "Alec Green" and when it was almost finished he showed it to a friend over dinner who happened to be the editor of the Burnley Advertiser, who persuaded him to let it be published (anonymously Hocking insisted) in the Burnley Advertiser. It caught the public's imagination, and Hocking cut out the columns and sent them to F.Warne & Co. asking if they would be interested in the book. Warne agreed and sent him a cheque for £15 for copyright to the book.

One afternoon he was called upon to present the Sunday School Prizes, and browsed through the book that they had decided to give that year as the Prize. Quite incensed by the descriptions in the book of all the street urchins being no-goods and thieves beyond redemption, and implying that they were there because of their own misdeeds, he rushed home and started putting down on paper what he considered was a truer picture of how these children ended up in their sorry plight. "There but for God could be each one of us" was his theme, and that night "Her Benny" was born. He persuaded the Editor of his church's magazine 'The Denominational' to reluctantly carry the story as a serial, they were worried that it would upset some of their older readers - it didn't, and was an immediate success and lifted the magazine's circulation and standing.

He moved to a church in Manchester, and fell in with J. Marshall Mather of the Manchester City Mission, who he met in the Friends Meeting House in Mount Street. He accompanied his friend on his trips feeding the poor, and found out the workings of the soup kitchens and night shelters, that the Manchester City Mission had set up.

"Manchester did not suit my health" said Hocking and after three years there he took up a post in 1883 at Southport and the challenge of the new chapel in Duke Street which had just been built to replace the old one on Lord Street. The Chapel was hopelessly in debt with only a small congregation, but he threw himself into the post and within 12 months the chapel had nearly 1,000 people every Sunday and were almost out of debt.

In 1895 he retired to concentrate on writing which by now was earning money for his charities. In 1923 he wrote his biography; a very rare book, it is called "My Book of Memories". Silas passed away on 15th September 1935 in Hornsey, Highgate, North London. **_CLIFF HAYES_**

CONTENTS

ꙮꙮꙮꙮꙮꙮꙮꙮꙮꙮꙮꙮꙮꙮꙮꙮꙮꙮꙮꙮꙮꙮꙮꙮꙮꙮꙮ

What the critics said about the book when it first appeared in 1875.

"The Rev. Silas K. Hocking is one of the not too-numerous band of Novel writers who know how to convey religious teaching without wearying the readers…"

MANCHESTER GUARDIAN

φφφφφφφφφφφφφφφφφφφφφφφφφφφφφφ

CHIPS.

CHAPTER I.

SATURDAY NIGHT.

SETH BAKER sat on the floor, trying to rub into his bare feet a sensation of warmth. Seth had been out all the day, and had succeeded in disposing of a tolerably large bundle of chips. It is true that he had met with a great many rebuffs, and night had fallen several hours before he succeeded in parting with his last pennyworth. Still he *had* succeeded, and though he was very tired and very hungry, he had cleared sixpence by the day's transactions, and, as a consequence, was in very good humour with himself, and with the world generally.

It had been a raw, cheerless December day, with

a rising wind, and a sky that had threatened snow since noon. And now, as Seth sat in a corner of his dark windy garret, rubbing his bare feet and listening to the moaning of the wintry wind outside, he fancied he heard also a sound as of snow being sifted on the broken skylight, and falling through to the floor.

It was too dark, however, for him to see anything, and he had no means of getting a light; so he sat rubbing away at his benumbed feet very patiently, giving a low whistle every now and then as the wind, in fitful gusts, went sweeping past.

There was no furniture in the room, not even a fireplace. In the farthest corner from the staircase was a heap of dirty shavings and sawdust, on which Seth and his brother Bob (or Chips, as he was always called) slept at nights; but beyond this there was nothing, if we except an empty ink-bottle, into which the brothers sometimes stuck a candle when they were fortunate enough to get one.

" I wish I had a match," said Seth to himself, at length, " an' I would look about me a bit. But, there! what's the use o' wishin'? If the snow is comin' in, it'll 'ave to come in, for the hole is too high up for us to get at; an' I'll have to wait 'ere till Chips comes, anyhow; but he's precious late, an' I'm nearly clemmed."

Seth might have been nine or ten years of age, certainly not older. He was a bright, intelligent lad, with large dreamy-looking eyes, and a shock of brown thickly-curling hair. His face, however, was pale and very thin, and there was a feebleness about his appearance that seemed ill-fitted for the rough and toilsome life he led.

Seth, however, was not the one to complain. Young as he was, he had already learned that the only way to get on was to take life as he found it, and make the best of it. He had never known any other home than the house in which he then lived. He and his brother had been obliged to shift for themselves ever since he could remember ; and though occasionally Chips would speak of another home in which he lived before he came to Bilkey's Court, where there was a piece of carpet before the fire, and a proper bed, in which he slept, and wonderful articles of furniture, the names of which he could not remember, Seth was half disposed to fancy that Chips had dreamed it all, and that he had never known any other home than that in Bilkey's Court. Certainly he could remember nothing of the sort, and so rarely troubled himself about the matter.

And yet to-night, as he sat alone in the cheerless room, with the wintry wind moaning outside, and no light or warmth within, he could not repress a longing that rose in his heart for something brighter and better than he had ever yet known. It was getting on towards bed-time, and yet how would he and Chips be able to sleep on such a night, with hands and feet benumbed with cold, and only shavings and sawdust to keep them warm ? He did not know ; but he supposed they would manage somehow, as they had managed before. Yet life was very cheerless, and the world to Seth just then seemed very dark and cold.

"I wish there was a meeting on somewhere's," he said to himself at length; "for it's allers warm at meetin's, and I do like to 'ear 'em sing about the 'better land,' as they calls it, an' the beautiful river, and the warmth an' sunshine, and the Saviour as comes to carry us there, if we're only good. My! but if it weren't for leavin' Chips, I wouldn't mind goin' there right away; that I wouldn't." And Seth stopped rubbing his feet, and sat for a long time motionless, staring into the darkness as if he saw something far away beyond the narrow bounds of the dingy room; and something very pleasant, too, for a bright smile spread itself all over his face, and his eyes grew wide with wonder.

"Goodness, now!" said he to himself at length, springing to his feet, "I've been noddin' a bit, I do believe; but that bit of a dream wur 'mazin' nice; but I'll 'av to stir my stumps, or I'll be gettin' cramped."

And Seth began dancing round the room, swinging his arms and beating his sides with his hands at the same time.

"Mercy on us, I forgot it wur Saturday night, an' that there is no fear of the guv'nor and missus turnin' up for long 'nough yet, so I'll 'ave a good turn at jumping while I 'ave the chance. I'm bound to 'ear 'em if they should come in; but, lor'! there's no fear of that, so 'ere goes." And Seth gave a leap in the darkness, alighting on a little snow-drift that had gathered on the floor.

"Oh, Jerusalem!" he ejaculated, "that's a cold 'un, an' no mistake. But 'ere comes Chips, or the guv'nor, or the missus, or the whole lot on 'em together; lor' massy, now, what on earth's up, I wonder?"

And Seth paused to listen. Certainly there was the sound of footsteps on the stairs, but accompanied by a peculiar rustling noise, the like of which he never remembered to have heard before.

" Queer!" he said, scratching his head vigorously, " I can't make it up no road. I've a good mind to shout—I will too, an' risk it."

So leaning over the rail, he shouted down, " Who's there, an' what's yer business?"

" All right, Seth," came the answer, " there's nobody 'bout, is there?"

" No; there's nobody but me. But how are 'e so late, an' what are 'e bringin'?"

" Come and give us a hand, and you'll soon find out," Chips answered; and Seth was soon tugging away at a huge bundle of straw that Chips had brought home with him.

" Oh, glorious!" exclaimed Seth, as soon as he had recovered from his astonishment and delight, " where on earth did 'e get this?"

" I'll tell 'e all about it directly," said Chips, with his head in the straw, and pushing hard behind. And by dint of a good deal of tugging from Seth and pushing by Chips, the straw was at length got up the narrow staircase, and deposited in the corner on the sawdust and shavings. This done, Chips produced a box of matches and a candle, the latter of which was soon lighted, and stuck in the neck of the empty ink-bottle.

" Now, my lad," said Chips, with a comical leer, " look at that an' howl."

"Glorious!" said Seth, stretching himself on the straw and kicking up his heels; "but where did 'e get it, Chips?"

"Chap from the country had a cartful of it," said Chips, "an' was taking it back home again, and so I axes him for a bit. 'How much?' says he. 'Oh, a a handful or two,' says I. 'What for?' says he. 'For me an' Seth to sleep on,' says I; and at that he laughed right out. 'Ain't you got no bed?' says he. 'Only sawdust and shavings,' says I. 'Lor' bless us!' said he, 'thou shalt have as much as thou canst carry.' And at that he twisted a long rope wi' the straw on his thumb in a jiffy. It *wur* curious. I never seen owt like it afore; an' before one could say Jack Robinson a'most, he had tied up all the straw wi' the rope you see there, and hoisted it on my head, an' then, whippin' up his hoss, he drove away, larfin' like anythink."

"He's a brick, anyhow!" said Seth, turning a somer-sault on the straw by way of expressing his delight.

"Right you are," said Chips; "but come, don't you wan't some supper?"

"I did afore you came in," said Seth; "but I'd nearly forgotten all 'bout it."

"Come, then, look alive," said Chips. "I bought a odd lot cheap at the 'Golden Grid,' and there's enough 'ere for to-night and to-morrow also." And Chips produced a miscellaneous assortment of pie-crust, plum-pudding, cold potatoes, bread-crust, bones, and odds and ends of meat of different kinds. Chips was quite right in calling it "a odd lot." But Seth pronounced it a supper fit for the Queen.

" Nothink like variety," said Chips; " I likes a proper assortment when I go in for buying wittles."

Seth made no reply to this remark: he was too busy with his supper to waste time in conversation; but when the repast was ended, he suggested that if they could stop the hole in the skylight and keep the wind and snow out, " they'd be as snug as the bo'-constrictor in the Z'logical Gardens."

" What 'bout 'im ? " said Chips.

" Why, don't you 'member," said Seth, " how the chap said as how the bo'-constrictor swallered the blanket to keep hissel' warm wi' ? "

" Oh, aye ! " said Chips, " I mind it now ; but how about stoppin' yon hole ? "

" Dunno," said Seth ; " it's too 'igh up, I guess. If we had a ladder, now."

" But we ain't," was the reply ; " but we can manage, I reckon, arter all."

" Which way ? " said Seth.

" You stand on my shoulders, an' stuff the hole wi' straw."

This was scarcely sooner said than done. 'Splendacious ! " was Chips' remark when Seth had completed the job. And Seth, after regarding it for some time with critical eye, remarked, " That the wind could roar now as much as it liked, and that they, in their new bed of clean warm straw, would be able to listen to it in comfort."

In this Seth was quite right. Long after the candle had burnt itself out the brothers lay in each other's arms, snug and warm, but not at all disposed to sleep. Outside the wind moaned and roared, and tossed the snow about in blinding drifts ; and as they listened to the weird wild music of the storm, they nestled closer together, thankful for their refuge of straw, and more grateful than many a child of wealth screened by damask curtains and covered with quilts of eider-down.

CHAPTER II.

CHIPS was two years older than his brother, and so regarded himself in the light of Seth's protector. Chips was a strong bony lad, with a broad face, large mouth, high cheek-bones, and eyes that seemed almost to look through you. Seth might occasionally be duped by the cunning of others, but Chips never was. To outwit Chips Baker in a bargain was what his companions never attempted but once. To outdo him in anything was a feat they rarely accomplished. He was capable of almost any amount of endurance; was swift of foot, strong of arm, and fluent of tongue. Hence Chips was often comparatively well-off while his companions were penniless and hungry.

It was a great trouble to Chips that Seth was so
thin and fragile, and very often he wished that he
could impart to his brother a little of his own strength.
Though Seth never complained, he knew very well
that he was often tired almost beyond endurance; and
frequently Chips grieved to see that he had little or
no appetite for supper, though he had tasted no food
since morning. Unfortunately, too, as time went on,
he did not seem to get any stronger. On the contrary,
if there was any change at all, he got thinner and
paler day by day.

Several times during the night in question Chips
was disturbed by Seth's cough, and when the feeble
rays of the Sabbath morning struggled into the dingy
garret, he lay for a long time looking at his sleeping
brother, whose face was nestled almost close to his.

"Might 'a been a girl, he's so purty," Chips murmured
to himself. "But I wish he wur a bit stronger. But
he'll be better when the warm weather comes, I daresay, so it's no use worriting." And with this reflection,
Chips nudged him gently with his elbow.

"Well, what's up?" said Seth sleepily, blinking at
his brother out of the corners of his eyes.

"There's a place down in Salford where they're
givin' a free breakfas' this mornin'," said Chips.

"An' a meetin' after?" asked Seth, eagerly.

"I don't know nothin' 'bout no meetin'," said Chips.
"All I troubles 'bout is the breakfas'. Will you
go?"

"Aye, that I will," said Seth, jumping up.

'Don't make no noise, if you can help it," said
Chips, getting up at the same time, "for if the guv'nor

or mother hears us, they'll stop us from goin' out as soon as not, an' search our pockets i' t' bargain."

" Aye, that's so," Seth answered. " But did 'e hear 'em come in last night ? "

" No," said Chips; " an' I didn't sleep for long enough. They must 'a been precious late."

" Guess so ! " said Seth, trying his best to fasten on a pair of worn-out shoes that were at least three sizes too big for him.

" What are 'e after ? " questioned Chips, in a loud whisper.

" Why, I'm trying to fix these 'ere boots," said Seth ; " but I'm afear'd it's no go."

" Put some straw in 'em," said Chips, " that'll tighten 'em, and keep yer toes warm at same time."

" Never thought o' it ! " said Seth, proceeding at once to carry out the suggestion, which proved a great success.

" Now, then ! " said Chips, " let's slip out quietly ; but most likely they'll be sleepin' sound enough, for they'd be sartin to be drunk as fiddlers when they got home last night."

This was quite true, for among the inhabitants of Bilkey's Court it had long been the custom for them to go to each other's houses in turn on a Saturday night, after they had been turned out of the public-house. But they were careful not to go empty-handed. Several large jugs were always provided, in which they could take away sufficient beer for another hour's drinking. And sometimes, if money were flush, a pint bottle of gin was also secured, in which case the drunken orgie extended far on into the Sabbath morning.

2

Among the grown-up population of Bilkey's Court it was held as an undisputed fact that no man could be happy unless he was drunk. Hence the chief ambition of their life was to get drunk as often as possible—not fuddled. No; to be merely "elevated" did not meet the case, but to be thoroughly and completely drunk. Hence many of the men worked industriously and kept sober all the week, so that they might go the whole hog on Saturday night.

John Baker and his wife were among those who believed in enjoying themselves on a Saturday night, whatever might be their experience during the rest of the week. Not that they often remained sober from Sunday to Saturday; for John Baker, as tinplate worker, could earn his thirty shillings a week without difficulty; and Mary, by hiring a sickly baby, and going out begging from door to door, could easily earn another ten shillings; whilst most weeks, by means of threats and abuse, they extorted several shillings from Chips and Seth. So that they managed to get drunk about every third day without much difficulty.

It required a good deal of scheming on the part of Chips and his brother to checkmate their parents, and even then they usually came off only second best. But they bore their defeat, as a rule, very complacently. Kicks and abuse had been a portion of their lot since they could remember, and they scarcely ever hoped for anything better.

They were always on the watch, nevertheless, and kept out of their parents' way as much as possible. Hence their anxiety to get out of the house unobserved on the morning in question; and in this they were successful.

Once in the street, they set off at a quick trot over the crisp sparkling snow. The morning was intensely cold, with a clear frosty sky, and a searching north-east wind that seemed to pierce one through and through.

"Jerusalem!" muttered Seth, "this are a sneezer, and no mistake!"

'Aye!" said Chips. "Christmas 'as come four days too soon; but give us your hand, Seth, and you'll be able to run easier." And hand in hand those two children of want trotted on through the quiet glistening streets, till they were in quite a glow of heat.

"There's the place!" said Chips at length, pointing to a long low building, around the closed door of which thirty or forty ragged and hungry-looking children were gathered. This number steadily increased, until, by the time the door was opened, a hundred hungry little waifs were trampling the snow, many of them with bare feet, and arms and chests exposed to the keen biting of the wind. They were very patient, however, on the whole; but when at length the door was opened they seemed to surge through in a compact mass.

Inside the temperature was gratefully warm, with a delightful aroma of hot cocoa and buns; and in less time than it takes to write it, they had ranged themselves on the forms in expectant rows, and were impatiently waiting for the good cheer that had been provided.

Several gentlemen and one or two ladies walked up

and down the room to see that all was in order, and to find seats for the late comers. Then one of the gentlemen mounted the platform at the end of the room, and a lady seated herself at an American organ.

"Jerusalem! I wonder what's up now," Seth whispered to Chips, giving him at the same time a nudge in the ribs with his elbow.

But before Chips could answer, the gentleman had rung a little bell, and every eye was strained in his direction.

"Now, boys and girls," he said, "we will sing grace, if you will all stand up. And after that the cocoa and buns shall be handed round, for I have no doubt you are most of you hungry and anxious to begin."

A general nodding of heads greeted this remark, and then the gentleman's voice was heard again giving out the well-known verse:

> "Be present at our table, Lord,
> Be here and everywhere ador'd;
> Thy creatures bless, and grant that we
> May feast in Paradise with Thee."

The singing was not very good, though Seth thought it delightful, and, hungry as he was, he would gladly have waited to have heard it sung a second time.

Chips, however, had a much keener appetite for food than for music, or, as Seth told him one day, he had a great deal more mouth than ear. Hence Chips was thankful when the singing was over, and lost no time in putting his teeth into the bun when it was handed to him.

It was a pleasantly painful sight, if the paradox

may be allowed. Pleasant to see how thoroughly the poor children enjoyed themselves; painful to look at their pinched haggard faces, and think of their sufferings day by day. More painful still to look on into the future, and wonder what they would become. Many of them would, doubtless, sink beneath the burden of their existence, and, before another winter came, would be laid away to sleep beneath the turf. But others of them would grow up to be men and women—grow up in homes of vice and wickedness, and be surrounded by scenes of infamy and shame. What would they become? There were little children in that company munching greedily at their buns, with round dimpled cheeks and blue innocent eyes, and sweet pouting lips that one almost longed to kiss— little innocents fit to dwell among the angels. What would become of these? Alas! that they should be trampled upon like the snow in the street until they become as foul. If before winter came again they should be sleeping in their graves, who could grieve? Better death than shame a thousand times, for if they live, who shall save them—who?

CHAPTER III.

A GOOD NAME.

"HERE, Chips," said Seth, after he had been munching diligently at his bun for a quarter of an hour, "I can't eat no more; will you have the rest?"

"Nonsents, Seth! you can eat one bun, surely?" said Chips. "I b'lieve I could polish off a dozen on 'em!"

"Then polish off what's left o' mine," was the reply; "for, I tell 'e, I'm licked complete."

"Well, sartinly it's a pity to waste good stuff," said Chips; "so pass it on." And in a trice the remains of Seth's loaf had disappeared down Chip's wide throat.

"Lor, what a mouth!" chuckled Seth, as he watched Chips stowing away the cake.

" Well, what's amiss wi' it ? " whispered Chips, with a broad grin.

" Makes me think of what the preachin' gent called it one day," said Seth.

" Well, what's that ? "

" A hopen sepulchre ! " said Seth, stuffing his fists into his mouth to keep himself from laughing outright at his own wit.

" Why, he didn't mean me, you goose ! " said Chips good-humouredly, nudging Seth with his elbow.

" Must a' meaned you," laughed Seth ; " for there ain't nobody about that 'as a mouth anywise ekal to it." And Seth laughed again till the tears ran down his cheeks.

" Shut up, you monkey," whispered Chips, playfully nudging him again with his elbow, " the gent's speakin' again."

In a moment Seth was all attention.

" After grace has been sung," said the gentleman, " we shall hold a short service for those of you who are willing or able to stay. No one will be compelled to remain ; and yet we shall be glad if all of you will do so."

Whether it was because the room was so cosy, or they remembered the cold wind and snow outside, or whether it was that they thought they would best show their gratitude by staying, certain it is that not ten of them left the room.

" I suppose you have all seen the Manchester Exchange ? " said the gentleman, when a hymn had been sung and a short prayer offered.

" Aye, aye ! I should think so ! " they shouted in chorus.

"Not the inside?" he asked.

A general shaking of heads greeted that question.

"I thought so," he went on; "and yet I hope you lads, when you get to be men and gentlemen, will do business on the floor of that great building. But I want to tell you that inside that great dome that you have seen from the outside are these words:

"'A good name is rather to be chosen than great riches'—that is, it is better to have a good name or a good character than lots of money. You haven't any of you much money, and yet, poor as you are, you may all have a good name. Into a neighbourhood in which I once resided there came to live a man and his wife. No one knew who they were, or where they came from; but as they seemed very respectable people, they were soon invited to their neighbours' houses, and received their visits in return. But after a while it was discovered that the man was a returned convict. He had been a bank manager, and had robbed the bank of a great sum of money, and so was transported; and when the term of his imprisonment was at an end he came to live with his wife in this neighbourhood, where nobody knew him. But when it got to be known who and what he was everybody shunned him; he was no longer invited to people's houses, or treated as he had been before, and he was glad enough to get away to some other place, where his character was not known. You see, boys and girls, he had lost his good name, and got a bad one instead. So that if you would have a good name, you must be honest.

"I read a story some time ago of a little boy who, playing marbles one day with some other boys, stole one of the marbles and put it into his pocket, and as the lad from whom it was stolen had a great many marbles, he did not miss it. After a while the lad stole a cake from his mother, out of a cupboard, and she did not miss that. So he got bolder, and stole some money from his father, and spent it in oranges and spice, and his father did not miss the money ; so he thought he might go on stealing without ever being found out. After a while he got into a milliner's shop as errand-boy, and in time he had to help to serve behind the counter. So he began taking money out of the till : at first a very few pence, then more and more. At length he was detected, and transported —sent across the ocean—and never saw his parents or friends again. Now, you see, all that came out of stealing a marble. Now, I want you who mean to be honest to hold up your hand."

In an instant up went a forest of hands.

"That's right," continued the gentleman. "And I want you to remember also that if you would have a good name, you must be sober also. In other words, don't drink. 'Drunkard' is a very bad name, but no boy or girl need be ashamed of being called a teetotaller.

In the next place, if you would have a good name, you must be truthful. People who tell lies always get found out sooner or later, and then nobody will believe them, even when they speak the truth.

"I see some of you are getting sleepy, so I will tell you a funny story I heard some time ago. A lad, finding both his father and mother out, thought he would make some toffee for himself, so he stole some butter and sugar out of the cupboard, and soon had it boiling in a pan quite ready to pour out. He thought, however, that he had better first see if the coast were clear, so he ran to the door and looked out, and was very much terrified to see his father coming along the street. What to do he did not know. The boiling hot toffee would have to be poured somewhere out of sight, and that quickly; and at length, in desperation, he poured it into his trousers' pocket. When his father came into the room he was jumping about as if the floor were hot. 'What's the matter, Jack?' said his father 'Nothing—nothing; oh, dear!' he cried. 'But there must be something wrong,' said his father. 'No, there isn't,' he said. 'Oh, dear! oh, dear! oh, dear!' And then he had to confess all about it."

For some time after this the laughter was so great that nothing more could be said. When, however, it had subsided a little, the gentleman went on again.

"You see, boys and girls, that wrong-doing always brings its own punishment. Always be honest; always tell the truth. And I want you to be kind also, and industrious and persevering.

"You will find it hard work to be good sometimes —we all do—but if we trust in Jesus, He will help us. We sing sometimes, 'Look ever to Jesus; He'll bring you safe through.' Years ago, when there were slaves in America, the poor slaves tried sometimes to make their escape to Canada. They knew if they could get there they would be free, but they knew nothing about the way. All they knew was that it was due north, and that if they would follow the pole star they would get there in time, unless they were captured or died on the road. So off they would start, travelling chiefly through the night, over hedges and bridges, swimming rivers and wading through swamps, but always keeping the pole star in view, until they crossed the river that divided the two countries; then they were free. Well, boys and girls, if we would be good and find our way to heaven, the better land, we must look to Jesus. He is our pole star, our only hope, our only Saviour. I heard of a wicked father that used to flog his little boy for going to church, but he could not flog away his love for Jesus. The little fellow used to sell apples at a railway station, and one day he fell on the line, and the train went over both his legs. He asked the doctor who was dressing his horrible wounds:

"'Doctor, shall I get better?'

"'No, my poor boy,' said the doctor; 'you are dying now.'

"'Then,' said he, with a faint smile, 'tell 'em at home I died a Christian.' And so he passed away.

"It was Jesus that helped him to be good and brave and to die in the faith of the Gospel, and He will help you, every one of you, to be good if you will trust in Him. Pray to Him for strength every night and morning, and He will comfort and help you here, and by and by take you to His beautiful home in heaven. Now, before you go home, we will sing together one more hymn. It is called, 'When Jesus comes.'"

Seth could only remember the last verse, but that
he never forgot, and many times during the next few
days he repeated the words over again and again to
himself:

> " He'll know the way was dreary,
>   When Jesus comes;
> He'll know the feet grew weary,
>   When Jesus comes;
> He'll know what griefs oppressed me,
>   When Jesus comes;
> Oh, how His arms will rest me !
>   When Jesus comes. "

Seth thought that morning the happiest of his life.
" Chips," he said, as they journeyed homewards through
the snow, " I mean to die a Christian."

" Do you ? " said Chips.

" Aye, that I do," he said earnestly; " though," he
added, with a bright roguish smile, " I don't intend to
die yet awhiles."

" I should think not," said Chips reflectively; " we
may get well-off in time; who knows ? "

" We shall all be well-off in the 'better land,' " said
Seth, looking serious again.   " I do like to hear 'em
sing and talk about Jesus an' heaven an' all the other
nice things."

" Well, for my part," said Chips, " I'd rather 'ave a
good feed than all the singin' i' t' Manchester."

Seth made no reply to this, and the rest of the
way they journeyed in silence.   They received only
abuse when they got home, but the peace in Seth's
heart did not pass away; and when he laid his tired
head upon the straw that night, he somehow felt

happier than he had done for many a day before. He did not talk much, but Chips heard him repeating to himself just before he dropped off to sleep—

" Oh, how His arms will rest me !
When Jesus comes."

CHAPTER IV.

FOR the next three or four days Chips and Seth followed their usual employment, though with varying success. Chips generally managed to dispose of his bundle by dark; but Seth was not such a good salesman. If to the question, "Any chips to-day, mum?" he received the answer, "No, my lad," he would turn away without another word. But Chips, on the contrary, would have his bundle on the door-step in a moment, and would open a conversation something to the following effect:

"Not to-day, mum? Well, now, that *is* unfortunate. These chips I has is special good ones; I selected 'em myself, and can guarantee 'em all sound, mum. 'You 'ave some already?' just so, mum, but chips is always wanted, an' these 'll keep, mum; an' I don't know when I may 'ave such a good lot again. 'How do I sell 'em?' well, mum, generally I sells twelve bundles for a penny, but as it's you, mum, an' Christmas-time, I'll say thirteen as twelve. I can't afford to do it as a general thing, mum, but as the gents say at the big shops, I want to clear out surplus stock. 'An old hand,' am I, mum? Well, you see, I has to get my own livin' in an honest way, mum, and I'm quite sartin you'll find these chips all I says, mum. 'Two pennorth,' you say? Yes, mum, thirteen as twelve; I stick to my word, mum. A threepenny bit this" (putting the coin into his mouth). "You may as well take another pennorth: there you are, mum; saves the trouble of givin' change, you see. Good evenin', mum, and much obliged." And Chips would doff his cap, and walk away with an air of great satisfaction.

Meanwhile poor little Seth would be tramping from door to door, his bundle growing very little lighter as the day wore away. Sometimes Chips would go in search of Seth when he had disposed of his own stock, and if he were fortunate enough to find him, would give Seth a few lessons in the art of "chip-selling," for which the little fellow would be very thankful, though he never profited very much by it.

On the afternoon of Christmas Eve, Chips and Seth started from the timber-yard (where they were allowed by the foreman, who knew them well, to gather up what odds and ends of broken wood they could find) in different directions. Seth had been very poorly all the day. At breakfast-time he had scarcely been able to eat a morsel of food, and at dinner-time his appetite was no better, so that when he started on his journey he was so weak that he could scarcely drag one leg after another. He tried his best, however, to carry out Chips' advice, and "keep a stiff upper lip;" but it was very hard work, and he thought he had never felt so weary before in his life. To make matters worse, the wind blew against him in strong fierce gusts, and the cold was almost more than he could bear.

"It's no sort of use," he said to himself at length, ' I can't manage it no road to-day, so I'll go home, and lie down a bit; maybe I'll feel better after restin' a bit."

Fortunately Bilkey's Court was not far away, and dropping his bundle of chips at the foot of the stairs, he clambered up into the dingy garret, crept across on his hands and knees to his refuge of straw, and lay down, utterly exhausted, and completely out of heart. He felt very much better after a while, though he had no thought of venturing out again for that day.

The day was rapidly drawing to a close when his father came home hungry and excited. He had quarrelled with his master and had been dismissed, and, as a consequence, he was ready to quarrel about anything or with anybody.

"Hallo!" he exclaimed, stumbling over Seth's bundle of sticks; "what's the meaning o' this?"

"Seth's poorly," replied his wife, "an' is gone up to lie down."

"Don't believe a word of it," he growled. "The

young vagabond is only skulking. I'll soon teach him another lesson." And going to the foot of the stairs he shouted, "Seth, come down this minute; d'ye hear? or if you don't, you'll wish you had."

"Yes, father," said the little fellow meekly. And a minute later Seth stood before him, trembling and tearful.

"What d' ye mean skulking in this manner, you young dog?" said his father, grasping him rudely by the shoulder.

"I didn't think it was skulkin', father," said Seth; "only I felt very poorly. But I'm better now."

"And it's quite time you were, I can tell you," said his father, striking him on the side of his head with his hard open palm, and sending him staggering against the wall. "Now, pick up that bundle this minute and be off with you, and don't dare show your face here until you've sold every stick; and mind you bring the money back with you also."

"Yes, father," said Seth tearfully. And the next minute he had shouldered the heavy bundle, and had gone forth into the cold wintry street.

An hour later Chips returned quite white with snow, and was allowed to sit by the fire down-stairs in consideration of the fact that he handed over to his father all his money.

"Is Seth home?" Chips asked at length.

"No," said his mother. "He's been home, but as he hadn't sold his chips, his father sent him off again an hour ago, and told him not to come home until he had sold the lot." Saying which, she followed her husband out of the house; for it was Christmas Eve.

3

and they had arranged for a carousal in honour of the occasion.

Chips was frightfully indignant at the treatment Seth had received, and sat for a long time staring into the fire, with an angry frown upon his brow. Outside the wind roared and wailed, and tossed the snow against the windows, and whistled through the keyhole, and rattled the badly-fitting door; and as Chips listened his anger blazed forth, and he began stamping round the room like a caged lion.

If there was anything in the world that Chips loved it was Seth. Perhaps he loved him all the more because he had nothing else to love. Seth was everything to him, and Chips was never happier than when the cheerful little fellow was poking fun at him or chaffing him, as he so well knew how to do. Chips was never angry with him. Angry! Chips would have been indignant at the suggestion. How could anyone be angry with little Seth?

And yet now, this wild winter's night, this evening of all evenings in the year, when children should be safe and snug at home, when in the homes of the rich the little ones would be enjoying themselves with music, and dance and song, his little Seth—his little fragile brother—was out in the storm and snow, with no one to help him, or pity, or bless.

"If I only knew where to find him," said Chips to himself, "I would start this blessed minnit. But I *don't* know—that's the rub; an' how tired an' cold the poor little chap will be!" And Chips proceeded to replenish the fire. "I'll 'ave a good fire for him 'gin he comes home," he muttered, "though father a'most kills me for burning the coal." And Chips drew up a rickety chair against the fire, and sat down, with a heavy heart, to wait the return of his brother.

As the evening wore away his anxiety increased: one hour after another he heard struck by the clock of a neighbouring church, and still Seth came not. What could be the reason? Surely he had not come home and crept up to the garret without his hearing him? At any rate, he would make sure. And Chips lighted a candle and bounded quickly up the garret stairs, and across to the bed of straw. But Seth was not there, and with a groan he turned away and slowly retraced his steps. When the clock struck the hour of midnight Chips could sit still no longer, he felt ready to choke. Something had happened to his little brother, there could be no doubt whatever. Perhaps he had been run over; or perhaps he had dropped dead in the snow—who could tell? "And here I be," moaned Chips, wringing his hands, "without a bit of a chance of helping the little chap."

And Chips went out and stood in the open doorway, and looked up and down the silent court. The snow was still falling, and the night wind was bitterly cold, but Chips did not heed it. All his thought was for little Seth. Where was he this wild, solemn night? Was he crying somewhere alone in the dark, with no one to help? Or was he beyond the cold and pain in the "better land," of which he was so fond of speaking?

"Oh that I could *do* some'at!" he moaned, looking out into the dark court with white anguished face.

Then it suddenly occurred to him that perhaps he

could pray about it.   It was true, he had never prayed
in his life; but at the meetings he had attended he
had heard the gentleman speak about prayer, and how
the Lord Jesus heard them, and would help them
when they were in trouble and difficulty.

"I can try, anyhow," said Chips to himself.   And
he went out and knelt down in the snow, and, looking
up into the dark wintry sky, he clasped his hands
together, and said:

"O Lord Jesus, please do look after little Seth.   I
don't know where he is; but if You come across him
anywhere, please give him a lift.   He's been poorly all
day, and father never ought to 'a sent 'im out.   I'm
afraid it 'll be a case wi' him, unless You take him in
hand.   Oh, please do just look him up, an' keep him
safe an' warm till mornin'.   Amen."

Somehow Chips felt all the better after giving
expression to his trouble in this way; and he was not
without a hope that the Lord Jesus would answer his
prayer.   He was still watching in the open doorway
when his parents reeled home, and, at the stern
bidding of his father, crept silently up into the dark
lonely garret, and lay down on the straw to wait and
watch for the morning.   It was the first night he
could ever remember being without his little brother,
and it seemed very strange and desolate.   Besides,
there was a great fear in his heart lest his little Seth
should never more share his bed of straw, and so he
lay, staring with glassy eyes into the darkness, and
starting at every sound that broke the stillness of the
night.   Scores of times, as the solemn hours dragged
slowly away, he fancied he heard Seth's footstep on

the stairs, and would start up and listen ; then, with a sigh, he would lie down again to fancy anon, as the wintry wind wailed around the house, that he heard his feeble voice crying in the darkness for succour and help.

Such a night as that poor Chips had never known before. Yet it came to an end at length ; and just as the day was breaking, worn-out with watching and anxiety, he dropped off into a dreamful and troubled sleep.

CHAPTER V.

CHRISTMAS DAY.

WHEN Chips awoke it was broad day, and the air was full of the wild melody of Christmas bells. For a moment he seemed bewildered, feeling sure that something had happened, but unable to recall what. Then suddenly the recollection of the drear night he had passed through came back to him, and, burying his face in the straw, he moaned, "O Seth, Seth, my little Seth, please do come home to me, or. I'll break my heart!"

Then for the first time he gave way to tears. "Oh, what shall I do?" he wailed, the tears streaming down his cheeks. "What shall I do without my little Seth? If Seth is dead, I hope I'll die too."

Then raising his eyes towards heaven, he cried out in agony, "O Lord! if You do care a bit for us—I mean us who are poor, an' 'ave nobody to help us—then jist take care of little Seth, and I'll never be glad enough as long as I live."

After a while he grew calmer, and hearing his father and mother moving about in the room below, he crept silently down the stairs and into their apartment.

"Oh, father!" he burst out, "Seth's never been in for the night."

"An' who cares for that?" was the savage reply.

"Don't *you* care?" asked Chips in astonishment.

"Not I, indeed," was the answer. "I'd be glad if the both of you were dead and buried."

For a moment Chips looked at him, his face flushing with anger and shame; then turning to his mother, he said, "And don't you care, mother?"

"Don't bother me," she answered, "the brat'll turn up all right, never fear."

"They can't be sober," was Chip's thought, "or they'd never talk in that way;" and turning on his heel, he strode out of the house. The Christmas bells were still swinging out their music on the wintry air, but to Chips they brought no feeling of mirth or gladness; they might sound joyously to those whose hearts were glad, but not to him. He only heard one deep tone in the chimes that sounded like a knell; he had heard it at funerals, he heard it now, sounding distinct and solemn above all the rest.

It was yet comparatively early, and the great city seemed almost asleep under its white canopy of snow. Chips wondered, as he hurried down Shude Hill, that there were so few people abroad, and when he got into Market Street his wonder increased. A few solemn policemen were moving hither and thither, tracking the white carpet under their feet; but they were about the only visible signs of life.

"I can't make it up no road," said Chips to himself. "Bells a-ringin' an' nobody about! What's up, I wonder?"

Poor Chips! In his grief and anxiety he had forgotten that it was Christmas Day. He had hoped, when he left home, that he would meet with some newspaper boys of his acquaintance, and get to know from them if there was anything in the papers about any boy having been lost, or run over, or killed; hence he was greatly disappointed at finding nobody about.

For a long time he stood at a street-corner, wondering what he should do next. Then it suddenly occurred to him that perhaps Seth had got hurt, and had been taken to the infirmary.

"I'll go and see, any'ow," he said, bounding up Market Street at a rate that almost astonished himself.

"Hullo, Chips Baker! what's up?"

It was a lad of Chip's acquaintance who spoke.

"Is that you, Bill?" said Chips, glad to meet with anyone whom he knew.

"Aye, it's me; or, leastways, I thinks it are. But what's up?"

"Seth's lost," said Chips, lowering his voice. "Father sent him out 'esterday aft'noon, and he's never comed home. What can it mean, Bill?"

"No knowin'," said Bill. "An' bein' Christmas, there'll be no gittin' to know, I 'spect."

"Aye; it's Christmas, ain't it? I'd clean forgot all 'bout it," said Chips. "Still, if he's got hurt, they may know some'at 'bout it at the 'firmary. At any rate, I'll ax; so 'ere's off."

But disappointment still dogged his steps. Nobody answering to the description he gave of Seth had been brought in, and, with a sigh, he turned away to prosecute his search elsewhere.

Passing a church later on in the day, the door of which stood open, he crept inside. He had no particular object in doing so, only he was tired and cold, and almost heartbroken; and he was utterly at his wits' end to know what to do or where to go, and he thought—for hope had almost died out of his heart—that he would be as likely to find Seth in a church as anywhere else. The congregation had just commenced to sing as he crept noiselessly and unobserved into an empty pew and seated himself on a hassock, so that he might be out of sight. He thought he had never heard such singing before, and the music of the organ was wonderfully sweet. The words, too, somehow seemed very comforting to him just then, and he could not help thinking how Seth would enjoy it if he were there.

> " Art thou weary, art thou languid,
>   Art thou sore distressed ?
> ' Come to Me,' said One ; and coming,
>   Be at rest.
>
> " If I still hold closely to Him,
>   What hath He at last ?
> ' Sorrow vanquished, labour ended,
>   Jordan passed.'
>
> " If I ask Him to receive me,
>   Will He say me nay ?
> ' Not till earth and not till heaven
>   Pass away.' "

Chips could not make it all out, but he was satisfied that it referred to the " Lord Jesus." He had heard something before about " coming to Him, and being at rest," but it was not very clear to him yet.

Then came the sermon, and Chips heard, for about the second time in his life, the story of the Angels and the Shepherds, and the Saviour who was born in Bethlehem of Judea; he heard, too, about the miracles of healing He wrought, the loving words He spoke, and the beautiful home in heaven He had prepared for all those who loved and served Him. And Chips wondered "whether this good Saviour had taken Seth to the better country? whether, with his little brother, the 'Jordan was passed,' and he had found the everlasting rest?" From what the preacher said, this Saviour was more loving than anyboby else in the world, and in the home He had fitted up there would be no hunger, nor cold, nor pain, nor poverty, nor sickness, nor death for ever. And Chips thought that if Seth were really dead, and gone to Jesus, he was a lot better off; that he was away out of the reach of the wind and snow, and that he had found a Friend who would love him and take care of him for ever.

And yet, as Chips thought of these things, bitter silent tears trickled down his cheeks, and great sobs shook his frame.

"I oughtn't to fret," he said to himself, "if Seth's better off, but I can't help it,—he's all I has to love."

Chips crept out of the church just before the service concluded, and waited in the street till all the people came out; but little Seth was not amongst them, and with a great sob he turned away. He had tasted no food for the day, and was almost faint, but he never once thought of himself. If he could only find his brother, he would not mind going without food for a week. So up and down the cheerless streets he tramped hour after hour, resolved not to give up his search while there was daylight left in the sky. But it was all to no purpose. Of all the people he spoke to, not one of them could give him any information respecting his brother. So when at length the last glimmer of day had disappeared, he stole away to Bilkey's Court. His heart was well-nigh breaking, and he thought it would do him good to get away to his own dark corner and weep alone.

As he neared his home, hope revived within him for a few minutes. "It might be," he thought, "that Seth had come home during his absence." And with quickened steps he pressed forward, though his strength was all but gone.

At the door of the "living room," as it was called, he paused for a moment and listened; but no sound came from within, and pushing open the door, he found it empty. The next moment he was bounding up the garret stairs. At the top he paused again. Yes, there could be no doubt about it, he heard something moving in the straw: "his lost brother had come home," was his thought, and with a low cry of "Seth, Seth!" he sprang toward the bed. As he did so, something rushed swiftly past him and disappeared in the darkness; but without heeding it he dropped on his knees on the floor, and stretched his hands out over the straw bed, expecting to find his own little Seth; but Seth was not there, and with a groan that might have been heard in the next street, he fell prone upon the floor.

How long he lay there he never knew; but when he crept into his bed of straw, the warm place where the cat had been sleeping had grown cold again, and not a single sound broke the awful stillness of the night. Chips had given up hoping for Seth's return now.

"He'll never come 'ome no more ; oh, he'll never come 'ome no more !" he sobbed, "my little Seth ! my little Seth !" And so he lay throughout the night, rolling his head from side to side, and calling, in an agony of grief, the name of his little brother.

Chips never forgot that Christmas-tide. Years after he spoke of it with eyes brimful of tears : spoke of it as the bitterest drop in the bitter cup of his life, and wondered how he lived through those long hours of suspense.

If he had been certain that poor little Seth was dead and out of all his misery, he would have sobbed himself to sleep. But the awful uncertainty that shrouded his fate banished all hope of slumber, and compelled him to lie wakeful, suffering the acutest torture he had ever known. And when morning dawned at last, he stole silently down the stairs, with pale haggard face and wild bloodshot eyes, and plunged again into the wintry streets, to commence anew his search.

CHAPTER VI.

A DREAM OF HEAVEN.

WHEN Seth left his home — his father's threat ringing in his ears—and wandered forth into the fast-gathering darkness, he had no idea what direction he should take, and little hope of disposing of his burden. For a long time he wandered on quite aimlessly, keeping as much as possible on the sheltered side of the streets, but utterly indifferent to—and, indeed, unconscious of—the direction he was taking. The wind was very boisterous, and the snow almost blinded him sometimes; but still he pushed on in a dazed hopeless kind of way. His hands and feet were benumbed with cold, but in his head a fire seemed to burn, and on his heart a weight infinitely heavier than the burden on his back.

He had a vague half-defined idea that he had been wronged,—that he ought not to have been driven forth into the wind and snow, weak and ill as he was,—yet he had no thought of disobeying his father.

Chips would have hid the bundle somewhere until the morrow, and invented some kind of story with which to satisfy his father. But Seth was of different calibre, both physically and morally. So he plodded on through the blinding snow, going away before the wind as much as possible, until he discovered that he had got beyond the neighbourhood of shops, and was in a locality given up to private residences; but whether he was at Cheetham Hill or Brooke's Bar he seemed to have no idea. That matter, however, did not trouble him; to dispose of his burden was now his only business. So he went up timidly to the first door of a long terrace of handsome houses, and then to the second and third, and so on to the end, and in every instance the answer was the same; that is, when the person who answered the door deigned to speak to him, for in many instances the door was slammed abruptly in his face before he had time to speak.

In some of the houses he heard the sound of music and laughter, for the young people were making merry on Christmas Eve, little dreaming of the poor little shivering lad who was being rudely spurned from their door.

In the last house—as he was turning away—he heard the sound of singing, and paused again to listen. It might be that they were singing Seth's favourite hymn, or it might be that his own imagination supplied the words, but surely enough he heard them:

> " He'll know the way was dreary,
>   When Jesus comes ;
>   He'll know the feet grew weary,
>   When Jesus comes.
>
> " He'll know what griefs oppressed me,
>   When Jesus comes ;
>   Oh, how His arms will rest me !
>   When Jesus comes."

"Aye," he said, a smile spreading itself over his pale face, " it's very nice. I think I'll rest 'ere a bit an' listen. It don't seem as cold as it did when I started, so I'll be all right for a bit."

So he crept under the window, and throwing his bundle of chips on the ground, sat on them in a listening attitude. The snow was still falling, and the wind made strange weird music in the bare trees that grew all along the terrace, which Seth mistook sometimes for the music within ; but the feeling of cold and hunger had passed away, and on his face there was an expression of perfect content.

At length the sound of laughter fell on his ears, and he got up and crept close to the window. The blind was not quite down at one corner, and Seth could not resist the temptation of taking a peep within. He never considered whether it was right or proper. He had no wrong in his heart, so he stood there holding to the ledge of the window with his almost frozen hands, and devouring, with great hungry eyes, the bright picture within.

On the floor was a thick spongy carpet of warm

cheerful colours, and on the walls hung beautiful pictures, set (in what Seth thought) were frames of gold. A bright fire was blazing in the polished grate, flinging its cheerful ruddy glare across the room, while beautiful and well-dressed boys and girls were seated in the soft roomy chairs, or were moving gracefully up and down the handsome apartment.

Such a picture Seth had never seen before in his life. Oh, what bliss he thought it would be to lie on the shaggy rug before that blazing fire! Could heaven be a brighter place than that room within? he wondered, or could the angels be prettier or happier than those boys or girls? Certainly he could conceive of nothing brighter or more beautiful.

After a while he noticed all the children gather in a circle round the piano, while a beautiful girl, with long golden hair, sat down and commenced to play. Seth fairly held his breath to listen. It was not "When Jesus comes" this time, but something he had never heard before. Very distinctly the words fell on his ear, warbled forth by the pure childish voices within:

> " While shepherds watched their flocks by night,
>   All seated on the ground,
>   The Angel of the Lord came down,
>   And glory shone all round.
>
> " 'Fear not,' said He (for mighty dread
>   Had seized their troubled mind);
>   'Glad tidings of great joy I bring
>   To you and all mankind.' "

Seth did not understand very clearly what it meant, yet it was so sweet that he thought he could listen all night; and very sorry he was to see all the children at length leave the room, while a minute later a servant came in and put down the lights.

Creeping back to his bundle of sticks, he sat down again. He thought the children would come back again directly. Indeed, in a very few minutes they had come back, or at any rate Seth thought they had; for he heard again the tones of the piano, and the children's voices chanting the much-loved words :

> " Oh, how His arms will rest me !
> When Jesus comes."

But it might have been only the sighing of the cold wind in the trees, and the echo of the song that yet lingered in his heart.

He did not go to the window again. He felt so warm and restful where he was that he had no wish to move. He had slipped unconsciously to the ground and lay half - buried in the snow, with his head upon the chips, and a sweet smile playing round the corners of his mouth.

He had forgotten by this time all about the errand on which he had come—forgotten his father's anger and his own weakness. There was music all around him, and the white silent snow that was so gently covering him felt soft and warm. The fire that burned in his brain had passed away, and the weight upon his heart had gone. It was all peace now, and rest and content.

It was all dark around him at first, but after a while the darkness too began to pass away, and the music

4

that sounded as if from far in the distance, began to come nearer and nearer, growing sweeter all the while. And, strangest of all to him, the wall of the house began to melt and vanish, and the beautiful room he had seen began to stretch itself out in all directions, until he found himself in the centre of a very fairy-land of beauty. And the flowers in the carpet lifted up their heads and began to live, and the golden frames of the pictures became the gateways to other scenes of loveliness that stretched away as far as eye could reach, and instead of a dozen or twenty children, there were hundreds, dressed in the most beautiful raiment he had ever seen, and carrying in their hands the loveliest flowers; and as he lay there wondering at all he saw, one of the children came and touched him, and said in a voice sweeter than any music he had ever heard, " Come, Seth, will you not join us, for it is morning now ? " And Seth got up and looked around him, and, lo! all the darkness had passed away, and the trees were no longer bare, but covered with the most beautiful leaves, and in the distance there rolled down a river, with water clear as the clearest glass, and on its sunny banks hundreds of happy children were at play.

Seth thought he would very much like to join them; but how could he ? He was only a poor chip-boy, and his clothes were dirty and torn. And yet suddenly he found himself upon its brink and looking down into its clear crystal depths, in which he saw the reflection of himself. Could it be possible ? Certainly it was his own face; for he had looked at himself many times in shop windows, and recognized himself again without difficulty. But his clothes were no longer dirty or torn; on the contrary, he was dressed like the other children in the most beautiful attire.

"Well, this is nice," said Seth, turning to his companion. "I never had so nice a dream before. I should like it to last for ever."

"And your wish shall be granted," said his companion.

And all the children began to sing as they gathered round him, till the air was full of music again; and in the trees above his head there was a rush as of angels' wings, and the snowflakes fell silently still. But Seth did not know it now.

There he lay, with his head upon the chips, a happy smile upon his face, and his eyes wide open; and still the snow came down like feathers from angels' wings, and gently covered up his white gentle face, and hid his rags from human gaze. And so at the last little Seth Baker, the chip - boy, was clad in white raiment, and had gone home to die no more.

An hour later carriages were driven up to the gate, and as the children tripped down the garden path to the carriages that were waiting, they said to each other, "Only look! See how the snow has drifted under the window! Did you ever see such a curious drift?"

They did not know that little Seth was sleeping there. It was well, perhaps, they did not know, for he was beyond their succour and compassion now, and was better off than they.

In their downy beds they fell asleep, and awoke in
the morning to the sound of Christmas bells, while
Seth, from his bed of snow, woke up to the music
of heaven, and to the joy that would last for
ever.

CHAPTER VII.

"HI, Dick, is there owt in the paper this mornin' about Seth, do 'e think?"

"Dunno, Chips," answered the news-boy; "but there's some'at on the pla-card 'bout somebody found dead i' t' snow."

"Oh, dear!" said Chips, turning pale. "I wonder if it is Seth?"

"Caan't say," said the boy; "but 'ere's a paper; read it for yoursel'."

Just then a gentleman came up and bought a paper, and was turning away when Chips touched him on the arm.

"If you please, sir," he said, "will you read in the paper what's said 'bout somebody found dead in the snow, for I'm fear'd it's my little brother."

53

"I shall be sorry if it's your brother," said the gentleman, opening out the paper and searching for the paragraph. "Oh, here it is;" and he commenced to read, while Chips listened with eyes and mouth wide open.

"'Yesterday morning as Mr. Maclaver and family, of Rodney Terrace, Victoria Park, were leaving their home for church, they noticed what seemed a peculiarly shaped snow-drift under their drawing-room window. On the snow being removed, however, a lad of eight or nine years of age was discovered, quite dead, with his head resting upon a bundle of chips. The body was at once removed to the "Friendship Inn," where it awaits identification. An inquest will be opened to-morrow morning.'"

During the reading of the above brief paragraph Chips had grown as pale as a sheet, and when the gentleman had finished, he stood for several seconds as if transfixed, his eyes seeming almost to start out of his head.

"Are that all?" he gasped at length.

"Yes, my lad; that's all. Do you think it is your brother?"

"Aye, it's Seth, sure 'nough," he said, with a great gulp. The next moment he had pulled off his tattered shoes, and was bounding along Mosley Street at the speed of the wind.

He had tasted no food for thirty-six hours, and was almost faint from exhaustion; but he did not realize his weakness. He felt neither hunger nor cold. He only knew that his worst fears were realized—that his little Seth was dead.

On, on, he went, the snowy pavement seeming to fly from beneath him. He did not notice that people stared at him as he passed—he heeded nothing that was passing around him. One all-consuming desire prevaded his entire being. All else was forgotten.

The " Friendship Inn " was easily found. Yet when Chips stood before the landlord he was unable to speak for several seconds.

" Well, boy, what is it ? " said the landlord.

But Chips only stared at him, gasping the while for breath.

" Why, what in the world is the matter with the boy ? " said the landlord.

Then the words came in convulsive gasps. " You 'ave a little boy 'ere brought in from the snow ? "

" Yes, my lad. Do you know who he is ? "

" My ·brother, I 'spect; may I see 'im ? "

" Yes, come this way ; we are anxious for the body to be identified."

Up a flight of stairs, along a narrow passage, and into a large empty room Chips followed his conductor.

" There he is," said the landlord, pointing to a corner of the room, where, on the floor, a little figure lay outlined under a white sheet.

In a moment Chips was kneeling beside the prostrate figure. Then turning his beseeching eyes toward the landlord, he gasped, " I can't do it, sir; I can't do it."

" Can't do what ? " said the landlord.

" I can't pull off the coverin'; will you do it, please ? "

" Oh, yes," said the landlord, instantly complying with the request.

The next moment Chips was gazing at his little brother, whose pale sweet face was stiffened in the last long sleep.

Chips did not cry or start, or make a movement of any kind. There he crouched on his hands and knees as though he had been changed into stone, gazing with hungry eyes at the cold placid face that never again would beam upon him with smiles of welcome.

But for the deathly pallor one might have thought little Seth asleep. There was nothing repulsive about the calm set face. His eyes were closed now, but about the slightly-parted lips you could almost fancy a smile yet lingered, while every line of want and pain had been smoothed away by the cold hand of death. It would seem as though he had died without a struggle, or had been lulled to sleep by the music of the wind, and by the songs of appy children.

As Chips did not move nor speak, the landlord went away and left him, and returned again in half an hour, to find Chips wiping away his own tears from the pale face of the dead, and moaning to himself, " O Seth, Seth ! will you never speak to me no more ? Don't you know me, Seth ? I'm Chips, your brother Chips. O Seth, Seth, my little Seth !"

The landlord was so touched by the boy's grief that he led him away at length, and gave him food, and did his best to comfort him.

John and Mary Baker were more than a little concerned when they heard that Seth was dead, and received a summons to appear before the coroner's iury on the following morning. They tried, however, to put a bold face on the matter, and manifested no symptom of grief whatever.

In his examination John Baker made a revelation. Chips listened like one in a dream, scarcely believing his own ears.

"He was not the father of the children," he said. "In fact, he and his wife had never had any children. But they were his brother Robert's children. Chips had been named after his father, and had always been called Bob until the street boys of his acquaintance nicknamed him Chips, a name that had stuck to him. His brother Robert," he said, "was a good man, a kinder or honester had never lived; he was a very sober man, too, scarcely ever tasting drink; and his wife Jane was a good woman, and they loved each other dearly. They lived in a nice little house, and were very comfortable. One night, however, when Seth was about a year old, Robert's companions, who did not like his sober ways, made him drunk. It was said they drugged the beer: anyhow, he went home mad drunk. What happened nobody could . tell exactly. But next morning he was found asleep on the floor, and his wife dead, with her head upon the fender, and a great gash in her temple. When Robert was awakened, he was horrified. He confessed all he knew about it, which was very little; he had a vague recollection of striking her with his fist—he had never spoken an unkind word to her before—but that was all. Well, he was found guilty of manslaughter, and sentenced to five years' penal servitude; but the knowledge that he had killed his wife, whom he loved so dearly, broke his heart; in less than a year he had pined himself to death. Well, as Mary and I had no children of our own, we took Robert's, and have brought them up as our own. They have earned a little sometimes by selling chips. On Christmas Eve they both went out as usual. Chips came home in the evening, but Seth never returned again. That's all I have to say, and all I know about the matter."

Chips knew that the latter part of this statement was false; but he was so astonished at what he had heard that he was unable to say anything.

Mary Baker corroborated all that her husband said, and there were no other witnesses to call. The medical evidence was that death had resulted from exposure to the very severe cold, and the jury returned a verdict in accordance therewith. And there the matter ended.

Before evening little Seth was locked up in a cheap parish coffin, and hidden for ever from human gaze. Chips remained sobbing on the floor till the last screw was driven in, then crept out of the room, and made his way with slow and listless steps to Bilkey's Court. That was the last night he ever spent there. When morning came he presented himself before his uncle and aunt with a strange hard look of determination upon his face.

" An' so you're not my father ? " he said, addressing his uncle.

" No, I'm not," said John Baker ; " but what of that ?"

" On'y I'm glad of it," was the reply. " I'd rather my father were dead than be like you. I always told Seth I could 'member another home nor this; but you've killed him; but let me tell 'e you'll not kill me."

"You'd better not say that again, youngster," said his uncle fiercely, "or you'll rue it."

"It don't matter," was the reply; "you know 'tis true, an' it won't be very nice for 'e to 'member, I'm thinkin'."

"What won't be nice?" said John Baker savagely.

"Why, it won't be very nice, when the wind is a howlin' and the snow a-fallin', for 'e to think how you drove little Seth to death on sich a night."

For a moment ᵀohn Baker seemed to quail before the stern gaze of the boy. Never in his life had Chips dared to answer him as he was doing.

"I'm not afear'd of 'e now," Chips went on, "so you needn't glower. An' you can't harm little Seth no more; you've done your worst by 'im. You drove 'im out when he were weak an' ill, an' not fit to be out o' his bed; think on it, an' he a little fatherless, motherless boy! I didn't say nothin' 'bout it at the inquest; but I'm thinkin' your memory 'll punish 'e enough afore you die. I'm off now. I'm fear'd I should get to hate you if I were to live 'ere now, an' I don't want to do that. So good-bye. I'm not your boy, an' I shall never come back 'ere no more." And before John Baker had time to reply, Chips was gone.

In Rusholme Road Cemetery they found room for all that was mortal of little Seth. Chips was the only mourner present at the funeral. He waited in the keen wind that swept with mournful sound across the graves till even the gravedigger had gone, then with a sigh turned away, and bent his steps towards the city, for he had yet to find a place of refuge where he might spend the night.

CHAPTER VIII.

NEW ACQUAINTANCES.

TO tell how, single-handed, Chips fought the world during the next two months would take too long. And, indeed, none but him-self ever knew the sufferings and priva-tions he endured; for the days, as a rule, were cheerless in the extreme, and the nights bitterly cold; and, worse than all, the sense of his loss and the utter loneliness of his life made his lot doubly hard to bear.

But there is one little circumstance we must mention before we pass on. On the Sunday morning after little Seth was buried, Chips was admitted again to a free breakfast in the school-room already mentioned at

Salford. It was with very listless steps that he made
his way thither. He had spent the night underneath
a stall in Shudehill Market, and had felt very lonely
and sad : and when he crept out with the first glimmer
of day, it was with a dull pain in his heart that was
almost intolerable, and most sincerely did he wish that
he might die too—that he might be freed from the burden of life. He was, however, quite in time for the
breakfast, and crept in with the hungry crowd of
children, and made his way to the seat he had once
occupied with his brother ; for he had a vague feeling
that somehow Seth would be nearer to him if he sat
there. He had very great difficulty in keeping back
the tears that started in his eyes continually ; and
when at length all the children stood up to sing grace,
it was more than he could bear, and, hiding his face in
his hands, he sobbed as though his heart would have
broken.

By the time the buns and cocoa were handed round,
he had recovered himself again, and devoured speedily
enough the provisions that fell to his share. He felt
in better spirits, too, after being warmed by the cocoa,
and settled himself comfortably in a corner for the
service that was to follow.

The children seemed thoroughly to enjoy the address,
for the gentleman had evidently a large fund of
anecdotes at his command, with which he illustrated
and enforced the virtues of Honesty and Truthfulness
and Kindness, and Sobriety and Industry and Persever-
ance ; closing his address by urging them to seek the
help and friendship of the Saviour, who would never
leave them nor forsake them.

Then he gave them the opportunity of asking questions on any matter that they would like more fully explained.

For several moments there was no response. And the gentleman opened his hymn-book for the purpose of announcing another hymn, when Chips suddenly sprang to his feet :

"If you please, sir," he said, "if it wouldn't be too much trouble like———." Then there was a sudden stop, for his voice had grown husky and his eyes full of tears.

"Don't be afraid, my lad," said the gentleman kindly "we are all friends here."

"'Twern't that I was afraid," said Chips, pulling his sleeve across his eyes. "On'y my heart's been near broke lately, an' I thought, if 't'weren't too much trouble, I'd ax 'e to sing again, 'When Jesus comes.' "

"Oh yes, my lad, with pleasure," said the gentleman, "if you particularly wish it."

"The reason I axed," said Chips, "were because little Seth loved it so. You didn't know Seth, maybe ; but he were 'ere with me on'y last Sunday week. You must have seen him, I think. He was sich a bright little chap, was Seth, as full of fun as a guinea-pig, an' as happy as a cat in the sunshine. But he's gone now, sir ; I shall never 'ave my little Seth no more."

And Chips gulped down a great lump that had risen in his throat, and seemed for several seconds unable to say any more. Then he went on again :

"He went out to sell his chips on Christmas Eve, but he never comed back again. I watched an' waited for 'im all the night, but he never comed home. An all Christmas Day I searched for 'im, but I couldn't find 'im. Poor little chap! he 'ad got tired, an' lay down in a gent's garden wi' his head upon his bundle; an' the snow came down all the night an' covered 'im up; an' in the mornin' he were smilin' as if he were very happy; on'y his face was very white an' cold. But he didn't feel the cold, I reckon, for I guess he's in ' the better land.' "

And Chips began to sob again, many of the children keeping him company.

" I didn't mean to say all this," Chips went on after a while, in a tone of apology. " On'y the last time we was 'ere, Seth an' me, you sung, ' When Jesus comes;' an' you don't know 'ow it comforted little Seth. He kept sayin' it over to hisself all the way 'ome, an' afore he dropped asleep that night I heard 'im sayin', soft like to hisself:

> " ' Oh, how His arms will rest me!
> When Jesus comes.'

An' the last time we was out together, an' his bundle was 'eavy an' the roads was very bad, he went away singin', his face as 'appy as anythink:

> " ' He'll know the way was dreary,
> When Jesus comes;
> He'll know the feet grew weary,
> When Jesus comes.'

An' so I'd like for 'e to sing it again, sir, if it's not too much trouble, an' maybe it'll do me good; an' I'd be mighty glad if Jesus 'ud come for me, for I'm terrible weary."

And Chips sat down with a jerk, and hid his face in his hands.

Then the gentleman got up, and spoke a few words of sympathy and encouragement to Chips, and ended by requesting that all the children would join him in singing the hymn that had been of so much comfort to the little boy that had so recently gone to " the better land."

Chips was not able to join in singing the hymn himself ; yet it did him good, and he went away with a lighter heart than when be came.

Not far from the room he stumbled across a little cripple boy who was toiling wearily along on a pair of crutches.

" 'Ave you been to the breakfas' ? " said Chips.

" Aye," answered the little fellow, " I allers goes when I 'as the chance."

" Where do you live ? " said Chips.

" Long Mill Gate," was the reply.

" I used to live in Bilkey's Court, not far from there," said Chips.

" I know Bilkey's Court," said the boy.

" 'Ave you got any father ? " asked Chips.

" No ; but I've got a mother, and she's quite enough for me."

" What does she do ? "

" Gits drunk mostly."

" An' what do you do ? "

" Anything as turns up."

" What's your name ? " was Chips' next question.

" Joe Wigley."

" Shall I carry ye, Joe, for ye'll never get 'ome at this rate ? "

"Aye ; I'd be mighty 'bliged," said Joe, his eyes sparkling.

And the next minute Chips was bounding along the streets with the little cripple on his back. He scarcely felt his weight, while his heart felt all the lighter for doing this act of kindness.

In the days that followed, Chips often gave Joe a helping hand, for Chips was strong and active, and so was able to help the little cripple in many ways. And never did he stretch out his hand to help without feeling the better for it.

The gentleman who spoke to the children after their free breakfast never knew how much good his kindly words of counsel effected. In Chips they bore almost immediate fruit, and every day the lad tried to be honest and truthful and kind. If the gentleman had known, he would have been thankful indeed.

But Joe Wigley was not the only cripple whose acquaintance Chips made. There was yet another, who generally went by the name of " Old Ebenezer."

Ebenezer Wilks was about fifty years of age, but his hair and beard had gone quite white, which made him appear much older.

Ebenezer had been a cripple all his life, and for more than thirty years had spent his days in a little square waggon that ran on four six-inch wheels, which, by the aid of a couple of sticks, he was able to propel along the streets at a good rate. In this little waggon there was also room enough for a moderate-sized canister, in which Ebenezer kept his stock-in-trade, consisting chiefly of oranges, apples, toffee, and gingerbread nuts.

5

Ebenezer's toffee and gingerbread were always of the best kind—better could not be got in Manchester, and so in time he became noted for his honest dealings; and as he always looked tidy and clean, his trade rapidly increased.

Since his mother died, ten years before, Ebenezer had lived by himself, and, as far as he knew, he had not a relative in the wide world.

He thought of this sadly sometimes, and wondered what he would do when he would be no longer able to help himself. It is true that he had saved a bit of money; but if he were helpless, and had to trust the spending of it to the people around him, he knew that he would soon be penniless; and many a night the old man lay awake thinking of these things, and in his heart sincerely hoped and prayed that he might be taken at once out of the world when he was no longer able to help himself.

Chips had known Ebenezer by sight, and had known his name ever since he could remember; for at the time of which we write the old man was a well-known figure in many of the most busy thoroughfares of the city.

It was not, however, until more than two months after Seth's death that Chips and Ebenezer became acquainted; and as that acquaintance formed an important epoch in Chip's history, we will tell, in the next chapter, how it came about.

CHAPTER IX.

"OLD EBENEZER."

IT was a dreary evening in March. All day there had been a continuous drizzle of rain, sufficient to keep the streets in a state of chronic puddle. Chips had been out since morning, and was in consequence drenched to the very skin, and was as miserable —as he afterwards expressed it—"as he could live an' hang together."

In order to avoid the crowd, he was making his way along a narrow and unfrequented street, wondering how he should while away the rest of the evening, and where he should spend the night.

His experience of lodging-houses such as he could afford to patronize had not been by any means happy. It was only by the rarest chance that he could get near the fire, and if he gave up his clothes to be dried, he ran the risk of never getting them back again. More than once his pockets had been picked while he slept, and in other ways he had been fleeced of his hard-earned coppers.

On the other hand, to creep under the market-stall in his wet clothes, and lie shivering all the night, was a prospect not by any means inviting. Moreover, it was Saturday night, and the market would be open till late, so that he would have to wait till midnight before he would be able to creep unobserved to his place of hiding.

There were no cocoa-rooms open then where he might spend an hour over a mug of "grateful and comforting." The only refuge seemed to be the public-house. And yet, since he heard that terrible story about his father, he almost shuddered at the name of drink.

What, then, was he to do? That was what he pondered over as he made his way slowly along the murky street in the fast-deepening twilight. A little way ahead of him he heard the rattle of the iron wheels of "Old Ebenezer's" little waggon, as the old man slowly propelled himself along; for Ebenezer seemed in a very sober mood this evening, and was evidently in no hurry to reach his lonely home.

"Poor old Ebenezer!" said Chips thoughtfully. "Maybe he's as wet an' miserable as me. I wonder where he lives, an' if he's anybody to look arter him?"

Then Chips' thoughts returned again to himself, and to the questions that had been troubling him before. A moment later he looked up as a drunken man reeled past him, muttering curses as he stumbled on.

" I'll never be a drunkard if I can help it," Chips said to himself. " Oh, dear ! if it hadn't been for the drink, father an' mother an' little Seth might 'a been all livin', an' in that purty little 'ouse I sees in my dreams sometimes. Oh, dear ! to think drink's done it all; an' 'ere I be without a 'ome, an' without a friend in the world."

What other reflections Chips might have indulged in it is impossible to say, had they not been rudely disturbed by a great noise and clatter that arose in the street a little ahead of him.

Running hastily forward, he soon discovered the cause of the clatter. Poor old Ebenezer was lying in the gutter apparently unconscious, his overturned waggon close to his side, while three or four yards ahead was the drunken man who had stumbled over him, slowly, and with many curses, struggling to his feet, and midway between the two was Ebenezer's canister, with all his stock-in-trade, fortunately none the worse. The drunkard, with brain soddened and senses steeped in alcohol, evidently did not know what he had stumbled over, for as soon as he regained his feet he went stumbling on as before, without casting a single glance behind him.

Ebenezer was only stunned, and—thanks to Chips' strong arms—he was soon seated in his little waggon, with his all but useless legs tucked underneath him, his canister under his nose, and his face once more turned towards home. But the poor old man seemed dazed and bewildered, and, seeing his distress, Chips —always ready to do a kindly deed—volunteered to help him home.

"Aye, boy, I'd be so glad," said the old man, "for I feel quite mazy like."

"All right," said Chips, fastening his bundle-strap to the old man's waggon. "Where to?"

"Vixen Alley—off Ancoats. Do you know where it is?"

"Oh, aye," he said; and off he started, carefully dragging the little waggon and its occupant behind him.

By the time they reached Vixen Alley, Ebenezer had pretty nearly recovered from the effects of his fall, but he insisted on Chips going in with him and sharing his supper.

Chips was surprised to see how nimbly—by the aid of a pair of crutches—the old man moved about the house. A lamp was lighted—as Chips afterwards declared—in no time, and a fire was soon crackling cheerily in the grate. Chips was quite surprised to find what a nice little house Ebenezer had. There were pictures on the papered walls, ornaments on the mantelpiece, cushions on the chairs, and even some strips of carpet on the floor.

"Now, get into that big chair and warm thyself," said Ebenezer, "for I see thou 'rt wet, and I daresay thou 'rt cold."

Chips thought he had never sat in such a comfortable seat before in his life, and while he dreamily watched the faces in the fire, and conjured up all kinds of pleasant pictures, Ebenezer busied himself in getting supper ready. That done, he told Chips to pull round his chair to the table, while he nimbly hoisted himself on another chair on the other side.

Chips could scarcely believe his own eyes when he looked around. Not only was there a white table-cloth,—what he never remembered to have seen before in his life,—but there were real china cups and saucers, and a metal teapot, while among the eatables were tinned beef, bread and butter, and even some sweet biscuits.

Ebenezer did not eat much himself, but he helped Chips largely, and watched him closely while he was eating. Chips was by no means good-looking; but he had an open, frank, pleasant face notwithstanding, and Ebenezer was evidently much pleased with his new acquaintance.

When Chips had finished eating, Ebenezer opened a conversation, or, more correctly, began to ply his guest with questions.

" You're a decent-looking lad, and I'm much obliged to you for your kindness to me," he began; "and so you'll excuse me if I ask you a few questions. In the first place, where do you live ? "

" Nowhere regular," said Chips, blushing. " Fact is, I ain't got no home."

" Where are you're parents ? "

" Dead."

" Any brothers or sisters ? "

" Not now," said Chips huskily. " Seth died back at Christmas, an' I'm all alone in the world now."

"Ah, that's sad," said the old man. "But what's your name?"

"Chips Baker.

"*Chips* Baker! What does 'Chips' stand for?"

"Well, my real name is Robert, or Bob, but everybody calls me Chips now."

"Where are you going to sleep to-night?"

"Don't know," said Chips. "I often sleeps under a stall in the market, but it'll be late to-night afore the coast is clear."

"You're in no hurry to get home, then?"

Chips smiled feebly as he answered, "Oh, no; I'm in no hurry to get 'ome."

"Very good. Then perhaps you would not mind staying and helping me a bit? I've some toffee to make to-night, and I feel a bit mazy still, somehow."

"I'll be very glad to stay," said Chips, his face beaming with pleasure.

"Then stay, my lad," said the old man cheerily. "And now let's to work." And in a very short time Chips was initiated into the mysteries of toffee-making.

Chips never remembered an evening to slip away so quickly and pleasantly; and when at length he rose to go, he did so with a feeling of regret—almost of pain. He had his hand upon the door-latch before Ebenezer spoke:

"Look here, Chips—Bob, Robert—no, I'll call thee Robert,—I'm much obliged to thee; I am, indeed. And upon my conscience, I don't like sending thee adrift at this time of night, so if thou'lt stay for the night thou canst sleep on the sofa, and welcome,"

Chips needed no second invitation. He made no reply, however. He felt that he dare not trust himself to speak, but he came back and sat down by the fire again; and far on into the night—long after Ebenezer was asleep in the room above—he sat there, wondering, at times, whether he was awake or dreaming.

The next day being Sunday, and a regular downpour of rain, the two remained in-doors, Ebenezer entertaining his guest by reading aloud from the New Testament. It was a new experience to the old man, and somehow, as the day wore away, he found his heart going out towards the orphaned homeless lad, whose broad homely face beamed upon him with pleasure and gratitude. Ebenezer had not spent such a pleasant Sunday since his mother died, and when he hoisted himself up the stairs that night on his crutches, after seeing Chips comfortable on the sofa, he felt as though he would like to have the lad with him always. There was such an honest expression on the lad's homely face, such a genuine ring in the tones of his voice, that it was a pleasure to have him about.

"Hi, Robert?" he said next morning, when Chips was about to start on his daily round; "you'd better come back here again this evening, lad, unless you find a better crib. I've nobody but myself, and there's plenty of room for us both; and if you like to come, you're welcome."

"I'm sure I'm much obliged," said Chips, the moisture gathering in his eyes. "An' I'd be very glad to come, on'y I don't like to put on your kindness in that way."

"Toot, toot, lad! say nothing about it. You've been kind to me, and one good turn deserves another Besides, you can help me a bit this evening, if you like to come."

"If I can help you, I'll be so thankful," said Chips feeling ready to cry. And away he went through the sloppy streets, with a lighter heart than he had known for many a month.

Stumbling over little Joe Wigley, as he was returning in the evening, he gave him a third of his profits as a kind of thank-offering; and little Joe, who had had but poor luck during the day, went on his way rejoicing. So three hearts were made happy that day, and *kindness* was the magic wand that did it all.

Chips found that he could help Ebenezer in many ways. And every evening there was always plenty to do. Not only had the toffee to be manufactured but there was the house to clean, the victuals to cook, and their clothes to be washed and mended.

Old Ebenezer was quite clever at all these matters, and soon put Chips into the way of sweeping the house, dusting the furniture, and even washing the clothes.

So time wore on; and wet, windy, blustering March gave place to April's sunshine and showers. And still Chips remained with Ebenezer, nor thought of leaving him. In fact, they had become essential to each other. Ebenezer got to love Chips as though he had been his own son, and his cheerless, childless life became brighter than he ever hoped or dreamed. While Chips, who had never known a parent's love, regarded the old man in the light of a father, and confided to him all his history, and all his hopes and fears.

But when May came in at last, with long bright days and warm sunshine, and breezes warm and gentle, an old longing returned to Ebenezer, a longing that had been his with every returning May, but which had never yet been realized.

" I'll speak to the lad about it to-night," he said, as he squatted on his door-step enjoying the evening's sunshine. " Maybe we could manage it together, and if we could—Oh! if we could, I think I should desire no more."

CHAPTER X.

"ROBERT," said Ebenezer that evening, as they sat over their supper in the deepening twilight, "I want to have a little talk with you, my lad, so we'll do no more to-night. It's the first of May to-day, and a glorious day it's been. I'm like a cat in one thing, Robert,—I love the sunshine. But every year for forty years, when May has come round, bright and warm and beautiful, I've had a great longing to go away into the country to live. Oh, I think if I could get away among the green fields and listen to the birds singing all the summer long, that I should live twenty years longer yet. I never spent but one whole day right away in the country in my life, Robert, and I think that was the happiest day I have ever known. But I was only a child then ; and every year the town has got bigger, and pushed the country farther and farther away. And for years now my poor old heart has been aching for a sight of the country,—real country, I mean,—but aching in vain."

"Never mind," said Chips cheerfully, " I'll take 'e away right beyond Cheetham Hill some day. There's country there—fields and trees, an' all."

"Wait a minute, Robert," said Ebenezer. "I'm talking about living in the country altogether. In the winter, the city and noise, and my little home here in this narrow court, are bearable ; but oh ! in the summer I want to see the streams flashing in the sunshine, and hear the music of the wind in the trees, and listen to the singing of the birds, and watch the contented cattle in the fields. O Robert, Robert ! I've read about it in books, and heard my mother talk about her home in the country, until my heart has nearly burst with longing."

"It 'ud be very nice, I guess," said Chips, " but I never hope for owt so fine."

"I grew flowers in a long box on the window-sill once," went on Ebenezer, without heeding Chips' remark, " but the court got so smoky at last that they all died ; and I think sometimes that I'll die too, if I stay here much longer. But if I had a little house in the country, with room to grow flowers, and vegetables, and trees, around where the birds could sing, then I'd be happy. I've been studying gard'ners' books for years, and I know the proper times for sowing seeds, and the proper seeds to sow; and sometimes in dreams I've fancied myself in my little waggon, or hopping round on my crutches, weeding the beds and watering the flowers. O Robert, Robert! will my dreams ever come true?"

"Dunno, I'm sure," said Chips, looking puzzled. "All you say 'ud be glorious, but the livin's to be got somehow, and there 'ud be nobody in the country to buy chips or toffee; so I can't see as 'twould work."

"But if we had a large garden where we could grow vegetables, and fruits, and flowers; and you could come into market twice a week to sell them? Think of that, Robert; wouldn't you look fine driving a nice pony and cart, like a young gent?" And the old man rubbed his hands with glee.

"But all that would cost money," said Chips, shaking his head; "an' I know nowt 'bout gardenin'."

'But I've got some money, Robert," Ebenezer went on. "I've done a good business for thirty years now, an' I've put away a few pounds every year. I do think we could manage; we could employ a practical gardener to do the chief part of the work. I could weed the beds and 'tend to the flowers, and you could help the gardener and come to market. Now, listen to this, my lad, and say what you think of it."

And Ebenezer read from that day's newspaper an advertisement of a cottage to be let, with a large garden attached, and situated about eight miles from Manchester and two miles from Buckley Railway Station.

"Well," said Chips, scratching his head, "I'd like it 'mazingly, but I'm fear'd it's too good to hope for."

"Anyhow, Robert, we'll have a holiday to-morrow, and go and look at it. We can get to London Road Station for the eight o'clock train, and you'll be able to lift me in and out of the carriage like anything; and won't I get over the ground from Buckley, that's all, lor' bless us! I feel fair young again at the thoughts of it."

Far on into the night Ebenezer and Chips chatted about the cottage and the garden and the joys of country life; and when they went to bed it was still to think and dream of country lanes and green fields, and rippling streams and singing birds.

The next morning dawned clear and glorious. Ebenezer and Chips were at the station half an hour before the train started, and when they got fairly under way, their excitement knew no bounds. A journey by rail was a new experience in the lives of both of them. Oh, what joy it was to leave the noisy, smoky city behind them, and to drink in the pure country air, fragrant with the breath of ten thousand flowers!

The country children looked curiously at them as they passed them on the road from Buckley Station, but to be stared at was nothing new in the experience of Chips and Ebenezer.

They reached the cottage at length,—Fern Cottage it was called,—and both fell in love with it at first sight; it seemed to them a veritable Paradise, a perfect little bower of beauty. We readily grant that neither of them could be considered fastidious! a thatched cottage on a lonely moor would have been a joy and delight to both. And yet few people would have denied that Fern Cottage was a pretty spot.

It stood at the foot of a wooded slope known as
'the plantation," and faced due south.   On the east it
was bounded by two close lines of poplars, and, behind
these, two other lines of sombre-looking pines.   These
trees had been planted by the late owner and occupier
— a maiden lady, six months deceased — for the
purpose of screening the cottage from the east winds.
To the west, and in front, was a large garden, divided
by a gravel path leading down from the front door to
a stream of clear water, that rippled pleasantly over
its stony bed all day long.

Both cottage and garden had been well kept, for
the old lady had taken great pride in both, and
sufficient time had not yet elapsed since her death for
many marks of decay to be visible.   Moreover, John
Pearson, who lived with his wife and only child Jane,
in a cottage near, had still given an eye to the place,
for in the late occupier's time he had been gardener,
groom, and general *factotum.*

Since her death John had been compelled to stick
to his last, for he was a shoemaker by trade, yet he
was not without hope that when Fern Cottage got a
new tenant he might be employed as of old.

The cottage might have been let twenty times over
had it not been so far from the station.   That seemed
the one great drawback in the eyes of all who had
come to look at it, though the agent saw other diffi-
culties in the way of its being well let.   The cottage
was too large for any of the working class in the
neighbourhood ; it was too small for people who could
afford to live in the country and keep a carriage ; and
it was too far from the station for business men, who

would have to go and return from the city every day
So for six months it had remained empty, and seemed
likely to remain so for many months more.

John Pearson was very civil to Ebenezer and Chips
and readily showed them all over the place, though
he much wondered what two such comical-looking
individuals could want with a place like Fern Cottage.
But he had heard such wonderful stories before now
about great people in disguise and rich people looking
like paupers, that he had come to the conclusion, before
he had answered half of Ebenezer's questions, " that
very likely the old man was as rich as a Jew."

So John was very civil and pleasant spoken, and
asked them if they would honour him by coming into
his cottage and having a cup of tea with their dinner,
an invitation which was gratefully accepted.

Then Chips and Ebenezer took a ramble in the
plantation, and it was wonderful to see how nimbly
the old man hopped from place to place on his
crutches, and a pleasure to watch his beaming face.
Both he and Chips were very silent, for their hearts
were too full for speech. Forty years had passed
away since Ebenezer had spent a day in the country.
And, oh, what a long stretch of wilderness those
years seemed to him, as he lay there under the
whispering trees, with his thoughts far back in the
past ! What a weary round of toil from day to day !
What hopeless misery and pain ! And now Chips
had come to him, or perhaps had been sent of God,
and with his help there was a hope at last that the
long dream of his life might be realized ; and as the
old man thought of these things, silent tears rolled

6

down his bronzed and withered cheeks, the first he
had shed for years. He almost wondered if he were
not dreaming—if those pleasant dreamy sounds of
wind and stream were not the imaginings of his weary
spirit longing to be free.

Chips had left Ebenezer to his meditations, and
had gone off on an exploring expedition on his own
account. Reaching the top of the hill behind the
house, from which an extensive view of surrounding
country was to be obtained, he felt as though he
would like to shriek for very joy and delight. And
very likely he would have done so had he not espied,
in a sunny hollow of the hill not far below him, little
Jane Pearson,—or Jenny, as she was always called,—
searching for primroses.

A sweet shy child was Jenny, with soft blue eyes,
and a wealth of flaxen hair. She made Chips think
of what he had heard about the angels. He thought
he had never seen so pretty a child in all his life.
He was strongly tempted to go down and help her
search for flowers, but his bashfulness prevented him;
and so he contented himself with watching her through
half-closed eyes as she moved about among the ferns,
all unconscious of his presence.

He did not know then that she was John Pearson's
child, for she had kept herself out of sight while he
and Ebenezer were in the house.

What a pleasant dreamy day that was! what an
oasis in the desert of their lives! and yet, when
evening came, it seemed to bring with it a sense as of
something lost—of a joy that had come and gone,
leaving only a memory and a regret.

Ebenezer did not sleep a wink that night, though he retired to rest early, for he was sorely perplexed as to what he should do for the best. To rent the cottage and garden—and he would need an adjoining field or two as well—would be an important undertaking. He might lose all the money that he had worked so hard to get, and striven so long to save. On the other hand, it might prove a great success, and by investing his little capital in this way he might be able to live in comfort for the rest of his days.

Moreover, after this glimpse of the country, he felt as though he could never endure the dirty noisy town again. He felt as though he had not room to breathe; and if now he gave up this dream of his life, he thought he would break his heart and die. So by morning he had settled the question for ever. And before the bright sunny month was at an end, Ebenezer and Chips had taken up their abode at Fern Cottage, and John Pearson had been installed as gardener-in-chief.

CHAPTER XI.

A FRIEND IN NEED.

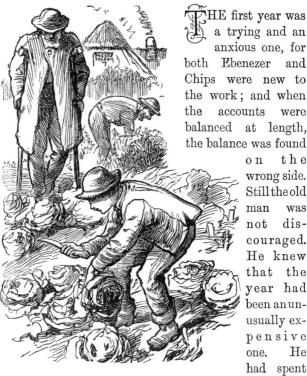

THE first year was a trying and an anxious one, for both Ebenezer and Chips were new to the work; and when the accounts were balanced at length, the balance was found on the wrong side. Still the old man was not discouraged. He knew that the year had been an unusually expensive one. He had spent a good deal in fruit-trees and in seeds and manure—

more than would be necessary for him to spend again ; and so he started the second year in faith and hope, and realized at the end of the year all he had hoped for

He and Chips were fairly on their legs now, and two happier mortals there were not on earth. They had reached the loftiest height of their ambition, had compassed all their desire, and so were content.

Twice a week Chips drove to market with his garden produce. And now he began to reap some little fruit from the hard and stony ground of his early experience. His customers soon discovered that they had no country bumpkin to deal with in Chips. He was quick, sharp-witted, and never lost an opportunity. But they discovered another thing : they discovered that he was strictly honest and truthful, and that if he recommended an article they might rely upon its being good. In the old days of weariness and want, he had proved by experience that honesty was the best policy ; but now, under Ebenezer's tuition, he had got to love honesty for its own sake, and was gradually growing toward a Christian life.

Chips never went into town without taking with him something for his little cripple friend, Joe Wigley, and Joe was always on the watch for his coming. The little fellow did not grow very much, and it was very clear that he would never be anything but a cripple all the days of his life. It was a sad destiny, though he never complained, and, if he could get food from day to day, seemed quite content.

So three years had passed away since Chips commenced to tread his new path of life, when one Tuesday he missed Joe from his accustomed place : he did not trouble about this at first, thinking he would turn up some time during the day. But though Chips waited about some time after he had disposed of all his goods, Joe did not put in an appearance. And Chips had to return to Fern Cottage without a sight of his little friend. He did not, however, make himself very uneasy about the matter, thinking that something must have turned up unexpectedly, and that he would be at the old place on Saturday morning.

But on Saturday morning Chips was disappointed again. Joe was not at the old spot, and Chips could not help fearing that something had happened to the little fellow—that he was sick, or had been run over, or perhaps killed.

"I must get to know what's up," he said to himself, striding rapidly in the direction of Long Mill Gate, having finished his business in the market. "If the little chap's in trouble, I must help him if I can. But how to find him's the difficulty."

It was a warm afternoon in June, with a soft gentle breeze in the country that was delightfully refreshing; but in Long Mill Gate, and in the courts and alleys leading therefrom, the air was stagnant and laden with the foulest smells. Chips felt as though he would be smothered, and wondered how, in the old life, he could have existed in such an atmosphere.

Going up to a group of ragged, sickly-looking urchins, who were playing pitch-and-toss with half-pennies, he inquired if any of them knew a little lad that walked on crutches, called Joe Wigley.

"I knows 'im," shouted one of the lads; "but 'e lives in Hangel Meadow, I'm thinkin'."

" Then you're thinking wrong," said Chips. " He lives hereabouts somewhere."

" Been down i' the pecker lately ? " queried another of the lads.

" Very likely," said Chipps.

' Mother got mar'red again an' cleared out ? " asked the same lad.

" I know nothing about that," said Chips.

" Lives in top 'ouse. 13 Court, top room, unless ow'd woman's turned him out."

" Thanks," said Chips, and started at once to find No. 13 Court.

This was easily done. It was a foul place. The whole court was reeking with all manner of uncleanness. At the top house an old woman was squatted in the open doorway, smoking a short pipe.

" If you please," said Chips, addressing her, " does Joe Wigley live here ? "

" Aye," she snarled. " I wish he didn't."

" Is he well ? "

" Aye, well enoo, only he won't own to it. But I'll bundle 'im out afore he's many days older, unless he looks arter gettin' the rent."

" Is he much in debt ? " asked Chips.

" Aye, goin' on a fortnight, an' his mother's cleared out for good an' all."

" What a shame ! " said Chips.

" Don't know," growled the old woman ; " he's better without her."

" Can I see him ? " was Chips' next question.

" Aye, if thou likes ; he's in the garret."

Up the rickety, rotting stairs Chips bounded, and

into the stifling garret. For a moment he could scarcely see anything, it was so dark.

"Who's there?" called a feeble voice from the darkest corner of the room.

"Why, Joe, what's the matter?" said Chips, going towards what seemed only a dirty bundle of rags.

Slowly the little fellow raised himself to a sitting posture. "Well, this is good of you, Chips," he said smiling feebly.

"Why, what is the matter with you?" said Chips, kneeling by his side.

"Dunno, Chips; on'y I feel clean done beat."

"Sorry for that," said Chips, producing a dozen large ripe strawberries that he had gathered purposely for Joe that morning. "Come, eat these, my lad, and you'll feel better, I'll wager."

"You are good," said Joe, smiling again; but though he tried his best, he could not eat all the strawberries. "I'll keep 'em 'gin to-morrow," he said, lying down again on the dirty rags.

"This will never do," said Chips; "you'll never get better at this rate."

"Don't much matter, I'm thinkin'," was the quiet answer.

"Oh, nonsense, Joe; don't talk in that way; never say die, my lad; keep your heart up, and you'll be well again in no time."

"Guess not, Chips; I'm clean done.'

"Not a bit of it," said Chips cheerfully, though he saw that Joe was very ill, dying for lack of fresh air and wholesome food. "I'll make it all right about the rent, and send up something nice for you to eat;

and when I come into town on Tuesday, I'll call again."

"I reckon I shan't be 'ere by then," Joe answered.

"Not here? Then where will you be?" said Chips with a laugh, though he felt more ready to cry.

"Nowhere."

Chips turned back again, and looked at him. "Are you in any pain?" he asked.

"No, Chips; never 'ad no pain."

"Hungry?"

"Not now: I was at first."

Chips turned away again, and walked toward the door. What should he do? He did not think Joe had any disease; he was simply exhausted, and if left alone much longer, he would die. What should he do? The old question came back again. Suppose it was little Seth who lay there, instead of Joe Wigley, what would he do then? That question decided the matter.

"Joe," he said, going up to the bedside, "if I were to bring the pony and trap round here, would you go home with me? I mean, do you think you are strong enough?"

Instantly the little fellow's eyes brightened. "Oh, aye," he said, sitting up in bed again, "I could manage that, I'm sartin."

"Eat up the strawberries, then, and this piece of cake, if you can manage it, and I'll be back for you in half an hour."

Chips wondered what Ebenezer would say. Still he felt that he could not do other than he was doing.

All the court turned out to see Joe off. The little

fellow looked very wan and thin, but his eyes were bright, and there was a hopeful smile upon his face.

During the first part of the journey he reclined in a corner of the trap quite still, with eyes half closed, and apparently taking no notice of anything. But when at length the noisy streets gave place to the quiet country lanes, and the wilderness of bricks and mortar disappeared, and instead broad vistas of country, clad in summer's beauty, stretched away until they touched the distant sky, Joe's eyes instantly brightened, and his face became radiant with delight.

" Oh, Chips ! " he exclaimed, " are this the country ? "

" Aye," said Chips ; " have you never seen it before ? "

" Never," was the laconic reply.

" Pretty, ain't it ? " said Chips, pleased to see his little friend so animated and interested.

" It's glorious," said Joe, gazing round him with wide-open eyes, and a glow of pleasure mantling his wan cheeks. Then he became quiet again, but not indifferent to what was passing around him. Now and then he asked Chips to stop the pony for a moment, that he might hear the birds singing in the trees, and after listening for awhile, he would nod his head, and Chips would drive on again.

It was a glorious evening. There was just breeze enough to bend the sedgy grass by the waysides and stir the foliage on the trees ; across the fields the hedges flung long shadows, and the slanting sunbeams fringed every moving leaf and blade with amber and gold. In the west the sky glowed like a furnace, and the few clouds that hung lightly in the heavens took

all hues and shapes—now vanishing almost from
sight, and now glowing as if washed in gold.

"Fine, ain't it?" said Chips, after he had driven on
a long time in silence.

"I ain't got no word as means it," said Joe, drawing
a long breath, and for the rest of the way he kept
silence.

He was quite exhausted by the time they reached
Fern Cottage, and for some time had lain on a heap
of straw in the bottom of the trap.

Ebenezer was getting quite anxious about Chips, he
was so late; but when he heard the noise of wheels,
he hopped to the gate on his crutches to meet him.

"Hi, Robert," he said, "thou'rt very late, my lad;
what's amiss?"

"I've been to see a friend," said Chips, "and
brought him home with me."

"A friend?" questioned Ebenezer. "I don't see
anybody."

"Here he is," said Chips, lifting out Joe in his
arms, and running with him into the house. Up the
stairs he bounded, and laid Joe in his own bed, and
then fetched a glass of milk, which the little fellow
drank eagerly.

"I couldn't help it, uncle," he said, turning to the
old man at length. "I found him all alone, dying for
want of fresh air and food. He'll get better here,
I'm certain; and I couldn't leave him alone to
die."

"You did quite right, Robert," said the old man
with evident emotion. "And I'm glad you've got
such a kind heart. Nobody ever lost anything by

being kind, Robert; and you'll get your reward for this, my lad."

For two or three days Joe's life seemed to tremble in the balance; then he began to rally, and in a little while he was able to get out into the sunshine, and to climb the hill behind the house. And long before the summer was over he was able to assist Ebenezer in weeding the beds and gathering in the fruit. So time went on, and Joe got quite strong at length. It is true he will always be lame, but he manages now with only one crutch, and sometimes he walks short distances with only a stick. To Chips he fills the place, to some extent, once occupied by little Seth, and neither Chips nor Ebenezer will ever hear of him leaving the cottage.

CHAPTER XII.

CONCLUSION.

CHIPS has nearly lost his old familiar nickname now. Ebenezer always calls him Robert, Joe and Jenny Pearson call him Bob, while John Pearson and his wife speak of him as Master Robert, or the young master.

The garden has been greatly enlarged since they went to live at Fern Cottage, and is now at least double the size it was formerly; and still they keep extending their borders while their business steadily increases.

A housekeeper presides over the domestic arrangements of the cottage now, assisted by Jenny Pearson, who runs in every day; and to at least one of the family she seems like a gleam of sunshine, and he is never so happy as when she is about. Chips has lost all his bashfulness, and Jenny is not nearly so shy as she used to be. Sometimes they may be seen in the plantation together gathering wild flowers, or sitting side by side on a mossy bank, engaged in very animated conversation.

Chips has grown to be quite a good-looking young fellow, while in mind and manners he has improved quite as much as in appearance. During the first three winters of his residence at the cottage, he spent four evenings every week at a night school in the village of Buckley, while he did a large amount of miscellaneous reading at home.

" It was not until he began to know something," he says, " that he discovered he knew nothing at all." And having found out that he had a mind, he set to work to improve it with all possible haste.

Chips is no genius or paragon of excellence ; but he is an honest, truthful, industrious, persevering young Englishman, and, in these degenerate days, that is saying a great deal. His face is browned by wind and sun, and his hands are hard with ceaseless toil ; but his heart is tender and his conscience clear. He makes no parade of his goodness, but he tries to do his duty in the sight of God and man.

He has never forgotten the simple little sermon on " A good name is rather to be chosen than great riches ; " and daily he tries to act out the teachings of the New Testament, and to trust in that Saviour who lived and died for all. He is not a member of the Royal Exchange yet, though he has stood upon its floor, and read the Scripture around its dome.

He has never seen his uncle and aunt since that memorable morning — well, no matter how many years ago. Months after, when time had soothed his sorrow, and the hard feeling he had cherished in his heart towards them had passed away, he paid a visit to Bilkey's Court, but the old home was inhabited by strangers. John and Mary Baker had gone away, but no one knew whither. He has made inquiries many times since, but without avail.

Old Ebenezer bids fair to live twenty years longer yet. He says, since he came to Fern Cottage, that he has renewed his youth, like the eagle. He has never visited Manchester since he left, nor has he any desire to do so. A few people were rather surprised at the old man's sudden disappearance, and instituted a few inquiries respecting him; but the multitude did not give the matter a second thought. It was reported at length that the old man was dead, and as there was nobody to contradict it, it was generally believed. Months after, when the old man heard of it, he rubbed his hands gleefully. " Dead, eh ?" he exclaimed; " why, bless us, I'm only beginning to live ! "

It would be difficult to find three happier people than Ebenezer, Chips, and Joe. During the bright summer days they spend all their time out of doors, going into the house only to eat and sleep. On summer evenings they may be seen reclining on a mossy bank at the end of the cottage, enjoying the quiet beauty of. the dying day. In the plantation they hear the birds singing their evening hymn of praise, while the brook rippling through the garden chants a pleasant accompaniment, and the evening breeze swells the song.

One by one the pale stars of God come out to deck the brow of night. The birds hush their songs and fold their wings to rest, but the wind still makes dreamy music in the plantation, and the brook ripples on as before.

At length the old man reaches out his hand for his crutches, murmuring to himself, but loud enough for the others to hear, " When I consider the heavens, the work of Thy fingers, the moon and the stars which Thou hast ordained, what is man that Thou art mindful of him, or the son of man that Thou visitest him ? " Then, after a moment's pause, he murmurs again, " Surely God is good."

" Aye, uncle, that He is," say Chips and Joe in chorus.

" Then let us thank Him, lads, and go to rest."

PRINTED BY MORRISON AND GIBB LIMITED, EDINBURGH